CHARLES RENNIE MACKINTOSH

FLOWERS

ADDRESS BOOK

Colin Baxter Photography, Grantown-on-Spey, Scotland

Larkspur, Walberswick, August 1914

NAME Animal Hospital
ADDRESS

TEL/FAX 404 252 7881
MOBILE
EMAIL

NAME Animal Control
ADDRESS

TEL/FAX 770 794 0358
MOBILE
EMAIL

NAME Alliance Theatre
ADDRESS

TEL/FAX 404. 892 2414
MOBILE
EMAIL

NAME Amelia Island
ADDRESS

TEL/FAX 904-261 6161
MOBILE
EMAIL

NAME Henry Bake Absher
ADDRESS

TEL/FAX 770 -344. 1925
MOBILE
EMAIL

NAME Air Conditioning
ADDRESS
AKA Decatur Heat/Air

TEL/FAX
MOBILE
EMAIL

NAME
ADDRESS

TEL/FAX
MOBILE
EMAIL

NAME
ADDRESS

TEL/FAX
MOBILE
EMAIL

NAME
ADDRESS

TEL/FAX
MOBILE
EMAIL

NAME
ADDRESS

TEL/FAX
MOBILE
EMAIL

A

A

NAME

ADDRESS

TEL/FAX

MOBILE

EMAIL

NAME

ADDRESS

TEL/FAX

MOBILE

EMAIL

NAME

ADDRESS

TEL/FAX

MOBILE

EMAIL

NAME

ADDRESS

TEL/FAX

MOBILE

EMAIL

NAME

ADDRESS

TEL/FAX

MOBILE

EMAIL

NAME

ADDRESS

TEL/FAX

MOBILE

EMAIL

NAME

ADDRESS

TEL/FAX

MOBILE

EMAIL

NAME

ADDRESS

TEL/FAX

MOBILE

EMAIL

NAME

ADDRESS

TEL/FAX

MOBILE

EMAIL

NAME

ADDRESS

TEL/FAX

MOBILE

EMAIL

NAME

ADDRESS

TEL/FAX

MOBILE

EMAIL

NAME

ADDRESS

TEL/FAX

MOBILE

EMAIL

NAME

ADDRESS

TEL/FAX

MOBILE

EMAIL

NAME

ADDRESS

TEL/FAX

MOBILE

EMAIL

A

NAME

ADDRESS

TEL/FAX

MOBILE

EMAIL

NAME

ADDRESS

TEL/FAX

MOBILE

EMAIL

NAME

ADDRESS

TEL/FAX

MOBILE

EMAIL

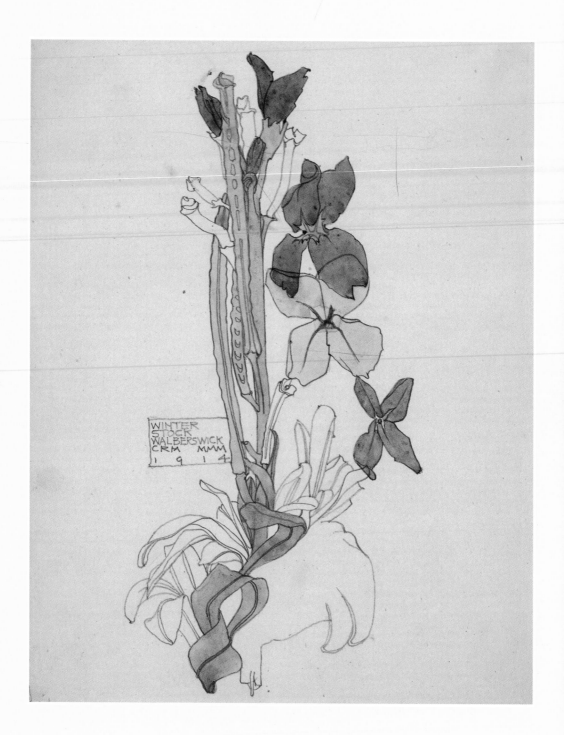

Winter Stock, Walberswick, 1914

NAME Rod + Annabel Boswell

ADDRESS

TEL/FAX 0926 84 2365

MOBILE

EMAIL

NAME John + Anna Bullock

ADDRESS

TEL/FAX 078583 3427

MOBILE

EMAIL

NAME Big Canoe

ADDRESS

South Gate 706·268·3376
North Gate 706 268 3399
TEL/FAX Entry 706 268 3331
MOBILE Golf 770 893 1200

EMAIL

NAME British Airways

ADDRESS

TEL/FAX 1·800 -247 9297

MOBILE

EMAIL

NAME Sara Barashick

ADDRESS

TEL/FAX

MOBILE

EMAIL

NAME David Barashick

ADDRESS

TEL/FAX 407-810 9965

MOBILE 770 801 7999

EMAIL

NAME

ADDRESS

TEL/FAX

MOBILE

EMAIL

NAME

ADDRESS

TEL/FAX

MOBILE

EMAIL

NAME

ADDRESS

TEL/FAX

MOBILE

EMAIL

B

B

NAME	NAME
ADDRESS	ADDRESS
TEL/FAX	TEL/FAX
MOBILE	MOBILE
EMAIL	EMAIL
NAME	NAME
ADDRESS	ADDRESS
TEL/FAX	TEL/FAX
MOBILE	MOBILE
EMAIL	EMAIL
NAME	NAME
ADDRESS	ADDRESS
TEL/FAX	TEL/FAX
MOBILE	MOBILE
EMAIL	EMAIL
NAME	NAME
ADDRESS	ADDRESS
TEL/FAX	TEL/FAX
MOBILE	MOBILE
EMAIL	EMAIL

NAME

ADDRESS

TEL/FAX

MOBILE

EMAIL

NAME

ADDRESS

TEL/FAX

MOBILE

EMAIL

NAME

ADDRESS

TEL/FAX

MOBILE

EMAIL

NAME

ADDRESS

TEL/FAX

MOBILE

EMAIL

NAME

ADDRESS

TEL/FAX

MOBILE

EMAIL

NAME

ADDRESS

TEL/FAX

MOBILE

EMAIL

B

NAME

ADDRESS

TEL/FAX

MOBILE

EMAIL

NAME

ADDRESS

TEL/FAX

MOBILE

EMAIL

NAME

ADDRESS

TEL/FAX

MOBILE

EMAIL

Jasmine, Walberswick, 1915

NAME Chateau Marmont

ADDRESS

TEL/FAX 323 656 1010

MOBILE

EMAIL

NAME Lyn Coltman

ADDRESS

TEL/FAX 770 457 8734

MOBILE

EMAIL

NAME Cobb Irrigation

ADDRESS

TEL/FAX 770 439 1067

MOBILE

EMAIL

NAME Bob + Carolyn Clarke

ADDRESS

TEL/FAX 01672 539 604

MOBILE

EMAIL

NAME Ed Craven-Smith

ADDRESS

TEL/FAX 01373 466 074

MOBILE

EMAIL

NAME Sue Chandler

ADDRESS

TEL/FAX 01905 24681

MOBILE

EMAIL

NAME

ADDRESS

TEL/FAX

MOBILE

EMAIL

NAME

ADDRESS

TEL/FAX

MOBILE

EMAIL

NAME

ADDRESS

TEL/FAX

MOBILE

EMAIL

NAME

ADDRESS

TEL/FAX

MOBILE

EMAIL

NAME

ADDRESS

TEL/FAX

MOBILE

EMAIL

NAME

ADDRESS

TEL/FAX

MOBILE

EMAIL

NAME

ADDRESS

TEL/FAX

MOBILE

EMAIL

NAME

ADDRESS

TEL/FAX

MOBILE

EMAIL

NAME

ADDRESS

TEL/FAX

MOBILE

EMAIL

NAME

ADDRESS

TEL/FAX

MOBILE

EMAIL

NAME

ADDRESS

TEL/FAX

MOBILE

EMAIL

NAME

ADDRESS

TEL/FAX

MOBILE

EMAIL

NAME

ADDRESS

TEL/FAX

MOBILE

EMAIL

NAME

ADDRESS

TEL/FAX

MOBILE

EMAIL

NAME

ADDRESS

TEL/FAX

MOBILE

EMAIL

NAME

ADDRESS

TEL/FAX

MOBILE

EMAIL

NAME

ADDRESS

TEL/FAX

MOBILE

EMAIL

NAME

ADDRESS

TEL/FAX

MOBILE

EMAIL

NAME

ADDRESS

TEL/FAX

MOBILE

EMAIL

NAME

ADDRESS

TEL/FAX

MOBILE

EMAIL

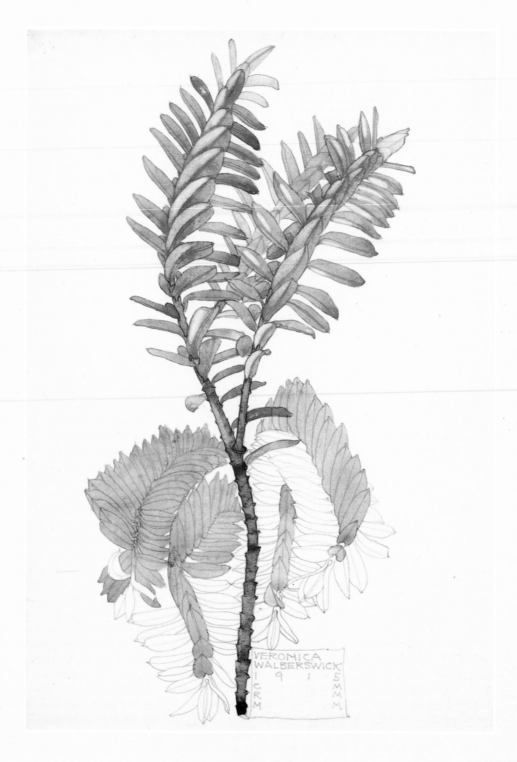

Veronica, Walberswick, 1915

NAME Delta

ADDRESS

TEL/FAX 404 765 5000

MOBILE

EMAIL

NAME Dolores Diehl

ADDRESS

TEL/FAX 770-394-9196

MOBILE

EMAIL

NAME Doctor Gamer

ADDRESS

TEL/FAX 404-256

MOBILE

EMAIL

NAME Amand + Dick Dame

ADDRESS

TEL/FAX 706-268-1285

MOBILE

EMAIL

NAME

ADDRESS

TEL/FAX

MOBILE

EMAIL

NAME Tony + Yvonne Dixon

ADDRESS

TEL/FAX 770-642 1810

MOBILE

EMAIL

NAME Ewan + Maggie Drake

ADDRESS

TEL/FAX 928 0994

MOBILE

EMAIL

NAME Dunwoody CC

ADDRESS

Golf (7) 394-1928

TEL/FAX

MOBILE

EMAIL

NAME

ADDRESS

TEL/FAX

MOBILE

EMAIL

NAME

ADDRESS

TEL/FAX

MOBILE

EMAIL

D

NAME	NAME
ADDRESS	ADDRESS
TEL/FAX	TEL/FAX
MOBILE	MOBILE
EMAIL	EMAIL
NAME	NAME
ADDRESS	ADDRESS
TEL/FAX	TEL/FAX
MOBILE	MOBILE
EMAIL	EMAIL
NAME	NAME
ADDRESS	ADDRESS
TEL/FAX	TEL/FAX
MOBILE	MOBILE
EMAIL	EMAIL
NAME	NAME
ADDRESS	ADDRESS
TEL/FAX	TEL/FAX
MOBILE	MOBILE
EMAIL	EMAIL

NAME

ADDRESS

TEL/FAX

MOBILE

EMAIL

NAME

ADDRESS

TEL/FAX

MOBILE

EMAIL

NAME

ADDRESS

TEL/FAX

MOBILE

EMAIL

NAME

ADDRESS

TEL/FAX

MOBILE

EMAIL

NAME

ADDRESS

TEL/FAX

MOBILE

EMAIL

NAME

ADDRESS

TEL/FAX

MOBILE

EMAIL

NAME

ADDRESS

TEL/FAX

MOBILE

EMAIL

NAME

ADDRESS

TEL/FAX

MOBILE

EMAIL

D

Japanese Witch Hazel, Walberswick, 1915

NAME David & Kathleen Ellis   NAME

ADDRESS   ADDRESS

TEL/FAX 404·252·5139   TEL/FAX

MOBILE   MOBILE

EMAIL   EMAIL

NAME Howard & Helen Elkins   NAME

ADDRESS   ADDRESS

TEL/FAX 770 434 4090   TEL/FAX

MOBILE   MOBILE

EMAIL   EMAIL

NAME   NAME

ADDRESS   ADDRESS

TEL/FAX   TEL/FAX

MOBILE   MOBILE

EMAIL   EMAIL

NAME   NAME

ADDRESS   ADDRESS

TEL/FAX   TEL/FAX

MOBILE   MOBILE

EMAIL   EMAIL

NAME   NAME

ADDRESS   ADDRESS

TEL/FAX   TEL/FAX

MOBILE   MOBILE

EMAIL   EMAIL

NAME

ADDRESS

TEL/FAX

MOBILE

EMAIL

NAME

ADDRESS

TEL/FAX

MOBILE

EMAIL

NAME

ADDRESS

TEL/FAX

MOBILE

EMAIL

NAME

ADDRESS

TEL/FAX

MOBILE

EMAIL

NAME

ADDRESS

TEL/FAX

MOBILE

EMAIL

NAME

ADDRESS

TEL/FAX

MOBILE

EMAIL

NAME

ADDRESS

TEL/FAX

MOBILE

EMAIL

NAME

ADDRESS

TEL/FAX

MOBILE

EMAIL

NAME Roger~Penny Fielding

ADDRESS

TEL/FAX 0161. 928 0872

MOBILE

EMAIL

NAME Fox Theatre

ADDRESS

TEL/FAX 404. 881 1977

MOBILE

EMAIL

NAME Ann Foulds

ADDRESS

TEL/FAX 0208 948 3377

MOBILE

EMAIL

NAME Ant + Beryll Fielden

ADDRESS

TEL/FAX 01254 245099

MOBILE

EMAIL

NAME

ADDRESS

TEL/FAX

MOBILE

EMAIL

NAME

ADDRESS

TEL/FAX

MOBILE

EMAIL

NAME

ADDRESS

TEL/FAX

MOBILE

EMAIL

NAME

ADDRESS

TEL/FAX

MOBILE

EMAIL

F

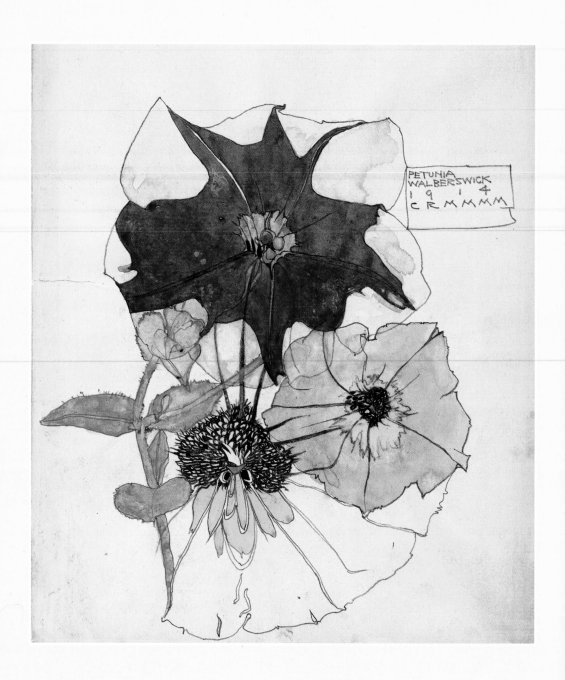

Petunia, Walberswick, 1914

NAME

ADDRESS

TEL/FAX

MOBILE

EMAIL

NAME

ADDRESS

TEL/FAX

MOBILE

EMAIL

NAME

ADDRESS

TEL/FAX

MOBILE

EMAIL

NAME

ADDRESS

TEL/FAX

MOBILE

EMAIL

NAME

ADDRESS

TEL/FAX

MOBILE

EMAIL

NAME

ADDRESS

TEL/FAX

MOBILE

EMAIL

NAME

ADDRESS

TEL/FAX

MOBILE

EMAIL

NAME

ADDRESS

TEL/FAX

MOBILE

EMAIL

NAME

ADDRESS

TEL/FAX

MOBILE

EMAIL

NAME

ADDRESS

TEL/FAX

MOBILE

EMAIL

NAME

ADDRESS

TEL/FAX

MOBILE

EMAIL

NAME

ADDRESS

TEL/FAX

MOBILE

EMAIL

NAME

ADDRESS

TEL/FAX

MOBILE

EMAIL

NAME

ADDRESS

TEL/FAX

MOBILE

EMAIL

NAME

ADDRESS

TEL/FAX

MOBILE

EMAIL

NAME

ADDRESS

TEL/FAX

MOBILE

EMAIL

NAME

ADDRESS

TEL/FAX

MOBILE

EMAIL

NAME

ADDRESS

TEL/FAX

MOBILE

EMAIL

NAME

ADDRESS

TEL/FAX

MOBILE

EMAIL

NAME

ADDRESS

TEL/FAX

MOBILE

EMAIL

NAME

ADDRESS

TEL/FAX

MOBILE

EMAIL

NAME

ADDRESS

TEL/FAX

MOBILE

EMAIL

NAME

ADDRESS

TEL/FAX

MOBILE

EMAIL

NAME

ADDRESS

TEL/FAX

MOBILE

EMAIL

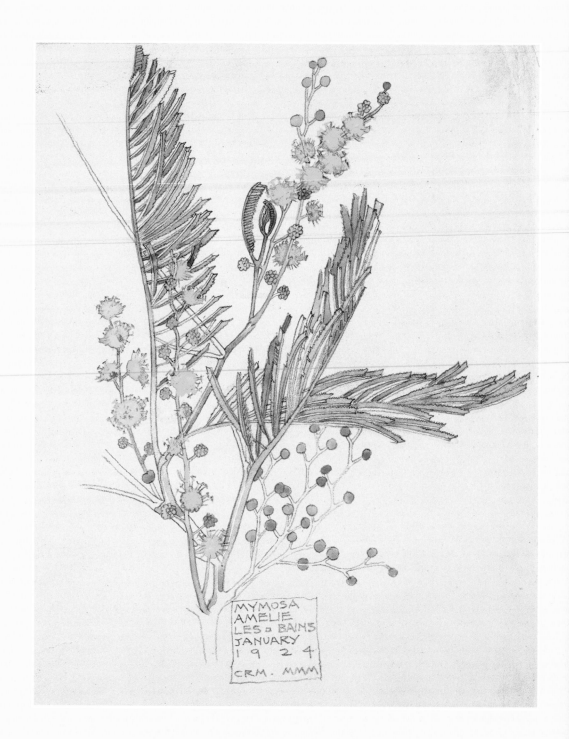

Mimosa, Amélie-Les-Bains, January 1924

NAME

ADDRESS

TEL/FAX

MOBILE

EMAIL

NAME

ADDRESS

TEL/FAX

MOBILE

EMAIL

NAME

ADDRESS

TEL/FAX

MOBILE

EMAIL

NAME

ADDRESS

TEL/FAX

MOBILE

EMAIL

NAME

ADDRESS

TEL/FAX

MOBILE

EMAIL

NAME

ADDRESS

TEL/FAX

MOBILE

EMAIL

NAME

ADDRESS

TEL/FAX

MOBILE

EMAIL

NAME

ADDRESS

TEL/FAX

MOBILE

EMAIL

NAME

ADDRESS

TEL/FAX

MOBILE

EMAIL

NAME

ADDRESS

TEL/FAX

MOBILE

EMAIL

NAME

ADDRESS

TEL/FAX

MOBILE

EMAIL

NAME

ADDRESS

TEL/FAX

MOBILE

EMAIL

NAME

ADDRESS

TEL/FAX

MOBILE

EMAIL

NAME

ADDRESS

TEL/FAX

MOBILE

EMAIL

NAME

ADDRESS

TEL/FAX

MOBILE

EMAIL

NAME

ADDRESS

TEL/FAX

MOBILE

EMAIL

NAME

ADDRESS

TEL/FAX

MOBILE

EMAIL

NAME

ADDRESS

TEL/FAX

MOBILE

EMAIL

NAME

ADDRESS

TEL/FAX

MOBILE

EMAIL

NAME

ADDRESS

TEL/FAX

MOBILE

EMAIL

NAME

ADDRESS

TEL/FAX

MOBILE

EMAIL

NAME

ADDRESS

TEL/FAX

MOBILE

EMAIL

NAME

ADDRESS

TEL/FAX

MOBILE

EMAIL

NAME

ADDRESS

TEL/FAX

MOBILE

EMAIL

Japonica, Chiddingstone, 1910

NAME

ADDRESS

TEL/FAX

MOBILE

EMAIL

NAME

ADDRESS

TEL/FAX

MOBILE

EMAIL

NAME

ADDRESS

TEL/FAX

MOBILE

EMAIL

NAME

ADDRESS

TEL/FAX

MOBILE

EMAIL

NAME

ADDRESS

TEL/FAX

MOBILE

NAME

ADDRESS

TEL/FAX

MOBILE

EMAIL

NAME

ADDRESS

TEL/FAX

MOBILE

EMAIL

J

NAME

ADDRESS

TEL/FAX

MOBILE

EMAIL

NAME

ADDRESS

TEL/FAX

MOBILE

EMAIL

NAME

ADDRESS

TEL/FAX

MOBILE

EMAIL

NAME

ADDRESS

TEL/FAX

MOBILE

EMAIL

J

NAME

ADDRESS

TEL/FAX

MOBILE

EMAIL

NAME

ADDRESS

TEL/FAX

MOBILE

EMAIL

NAME

ADDRESS

TEL/FAX

MOBILE

EMAIL

NAME

ADDRESS

TEL/FAX

MOBILE

EMAIL

NAME

ADDRESS

TEL/FAX

MOBILE

EMAIL

NAME

ADDRESS

TEL/FAX

MOBILE

EMAIL

NAME

ADDRESS

TEL/FAX

MOBILE

EMAIL

NAME

ADDRESS

TEL/FAX

MOBILE

EMAIL

NAME

ADDRESS

TEL/FAX

MOBILE

EMAIL

NAME

ADDRESS

TEL/FAX

MOBILE

EMAIL

NAME

ADDRESS

TEL/FAX

MOBILE

EMAIL

K

NAME

ADDRESS

TEL/FAX

MOBILE

EMAIL

NAME

ADDRESS

TEL/FAX

MOBILE

EMAIL

NAME

ADDRESS

TEL/FAX

MOBILE

EMAIL

NAME

ADDRESS

TEL/FAX

MOBILE

EMAIL

Rosemary, Walberswick, 1915

NAME Laura + Brian La Hill

ADDRESS

TEL/FAX 770 395 0108

MOBILE 404 556 2769

EMAIL laura@lahiff.org

NAME

ADDRESS

TEL/FAX

MOBILE

EMAIL

NAME

ADDRESS

TEL/FAX

MOBILE

EMAIL

NAME

ADDRESS

TEL/FAX

MOBILE

EMAIL

NAME

ADDRESS

TEL/FAX

MOBILE

EMAIL

NAME

ADDRESS

TEL/FAX

MOBILE

EMAIL

NAME

ADDRESS

TEL/FAX

MOBILE

EMAIL

NAME

ADDRESS

TEL/FAX

MOBILE

EMAIL

NAME

ADDRESS

TEL/FAX

MOBILE

EMAIL

NAME

ADDRESS

TEL/FAX

MOBILE

EMAIL

NAME

ADDRESS

TEL/FAX

MOBILE

EMAIL

NAME

ADDRESS

TEL/FAX

MOBILE

EMAIL

NAME

ADDRESS

TEL/FAX

MOBILE

EMAIL

NAME

ADDRESS

TEL/FAX

MOBILE

EMAIL

NAME

ADDRESS

TEL/FAX

MOBILE

EMAIL

NAME

ADDRESS

TEL/FAX

MOBILE

EMAIL

NAME

ADDRESS

TEL/FAX

MOBILE

EMAIL

NAME

ADDRESS

TEL/FAX

MOBILE

EMAIL

NAME

ADDRESS

TEL/FAX

MOBILE

EMAIL

NAME

ADDRESS

TEL/FAX

MOBILE

EMAIL

NAME

ADDRESS

TEL/FAX

MOBILE

EMAIL

NAME

ADDRESS

TEL/FAX

MOBILE

EMAIL

NAME

ADDRESS

TEL/FAX

MOBILE

EMAIL

NAME

ADDRESS

TEL/FAX

MOBILE

EMAIL

NAME

ADDRESS

TEL/FAX

MOBILE

EMAIL

NAME

ADDRESS

TEL/FAX

MOBILE

EMAIL

Blackthorn, Chiddingstone, 1910

NAME

ADDRESS

TEL/FAX

MOBILE

EMAIL

NAME

ADDRESS

TEL/FAX

MOBILE

EMAIL

NAME

ADDRESS

TEL/FAX

MOBILE

EMAIL

NAME

ADDRESS

TEL/FAX

MOBILE

EMAIL

NAME

ADDRESS

TEL/FAX

MOBILE

EMAIL

NAME

ADDRESS

TEL/FAX

MOBILE

EMAIL

NAME

ADDRESS

TEL/FAX

MOBILE

EMAIL

NAME

ADDRESS

TEL/FAX

MOBILE

EMAIL

NAME

ADDRESS

TEL/FAX

MOBILE

EMAIL

NAME

ADDRESS

TEL/FAX

MOBILE

EMAIL

NAME

ADDRESS

TEL/FAX

MOBILE

EMAIL

NAME

ADDRESS

TEL/FAX

MOBILE

EMAIL

NAME

ADDRESS

TEL/FAX

MOBILE

EMAIL

NAME

ADDRESS

TEL/FAX

MOBILE

EMAIL

NAME

ADDRESS

TEL/FAX

MOBILE

EMAIL

NAME

ADDRESS

TEL/FAX

MOBILE

EMAIL

NAME

ADDRESS

TEL/FAX

MOBILE

EMAIL

NAME

ADDRESS

TEL/FAX

MOBILE

EMAIL

NAME

ADDRESS

TEL/FAX

MOBILE

EMAIL

NAME

ADDRESS

TEL/FAX

MOBILE

EMAIL

NAME

ADDRESS

TEL/FAX

MOBILE

EMAIL

NAME

ADDRESS

TEL/FAX

MOBILE

EMAIL

NAME

ADDRESS

TEL/FAX

MOBILE

EMAIL

NAME

ADDRESS

TEL/FAX

MOBILE

EMAIL

Cuckoo Flower, Chiddingstone, 1910

NAME

ADDRESS

TEL/FAX

MOBILE

EMAIL

NAME

ADDRESS

TEL/FAX

MOBILE

EMAIL

NAME

ADDRESS

TEL/FAX

MOBILE

EMAIL

NAME

ADDRESS

TEL/FAX

MOBILE

EMAIL

NAME

ADDRESS

TEL/FAX

MOBILE

EMAIL

NAME

ADDRESS

TEL/FAX

MOBILE

EMAIL

NAME

ADDRESS

TEL/FAX

MOBILE

EMAIL

NAME

ADDRESS

TEL/FAX

MOBILE

EMAIL

MC
MAC

NAME

ADDRESS

TEL/FAX

MOBILE

EMAIL

NAME

ADDRESS

TEL/FAX

MOBILE

EMAIL

NAME

ADDRESS

TEL/FAX

MOBILE

EMAIL

NAME

ADDRESS

TEL/FAX

MOBILE

EMAIL

NAME

ADDRESS

TEL/FAX

MOBILE

EMAIL

NAME

ADDRESS

TEL/FAX

MOBILE

EMAIL

NAME

ADDRESS

TEL/FAX

MOBILE

EMAIL

NAME

ADDRESS

TEL/FAX

MOBILE

EMAIL

MC
MAC

NAME

ADDRESS

TEL/FAX

MOBILE

EMAIL

NAME

ADDRESS

TEL/FAX

MOBILE

EMAIL

NAME

ADDRESS

TEL/FAX

MOBILE

EMAIL

NAME

ADDRESS

TEL/FAX

MOBILE

EMAIL

NAME

ADDRESS

TEL/FAX

MOBILE

EMAIL

NAME

ADDRESS

TEL/FAX

MOBILE

EMAIL

NAME

ADDRESS

TEL/FAX

MOBILE

EMAIL

NAME

ADDRESS

TEL/FAX

MOBILE

EMAIL

MC
MAC

Stagthorn, Walberswick, 1914

NAME

ADDRESS

TEL/FAX

MOBILE

EMAIL

NAME

ADDRESS

TEL/FAX

MOBILE

EMAIL

NAME

ADDRESS

TEL/FAX

MOBILE

EMAIL

NAME

ADDRESS

TEL/FAX

MOBILE

EMAIL

NAME

ADDRESS

TEL/FAX

MOBILE

EMAIL

NAME

ADDRESS

TEL/FAX

MOBILE

EMAIL

N

NAME

ADDRESS

TEL/FAX

MOBILE

EMAIL

NAME

ADDRESS

TEL/FAX

MOBILE

EMAIL

NAME

ADDRESS

TEL/FAX

MOBILE

N
EMAIL

NAME

ADDRESS

TEL/FAX

MOBILE

EMAIL

NAME

ADDRESS

TEL/FAX

MOBILE

EMAIL

NAME

ADDRESS

TEL/FAX

MOBILE

EMAIL

NAME

ADDRESS

TEL/FAX

MOBILE

EMAIL

NAME

ADDRESS

TEL/FAX

MOBILE

EMAIL

NAME

ADDRESS

TEL/FAX

MOBILE

EMAIL

NAME

ADDRESS

TEL/FAX

MOBILE

EMAIL

NAME

ADDRESS

TEL/FAX

MOBILE

EMAIL

NAME

ADDRESS

TEL/FAX

MOBILE

EMAIL

NAME

ADDRESS

TEL/FAX

MOBILE

EMAIL

NAME

ADDRESS

TEL/FAX

MOBILE

EMAIL

NAME

ADDRESS

TEL/FAX

MOBILE

EMAIL

NAME

ADDRESS

TEL/FAX

MOBILE

EMAIL

O

NAME

ADDRESS

TEL/FAX

MOBILE

EMAIL

NAME

ADDRESS

TEL/FAX

MOBILE

EMAIL

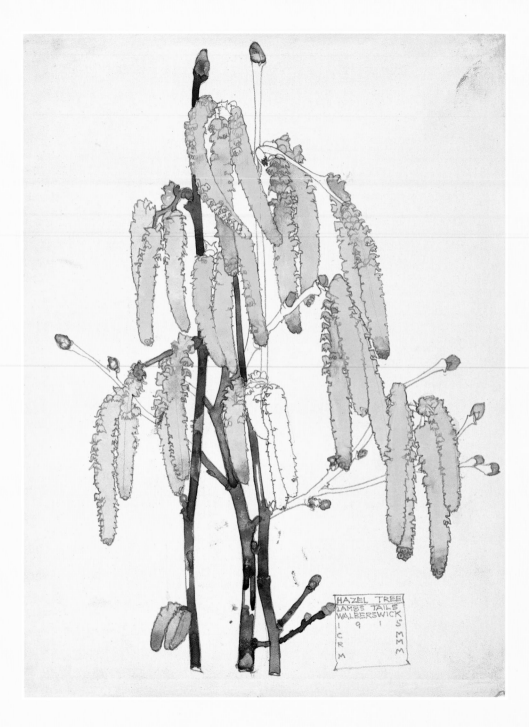

Hazel Tree, Lambs' Tails, Walberswick, 1915

NAME

ADDRESS

TEL/FAX

MOBILE

EMAIL

NAME

ADDRESS

TEL/FAX

MOBILE

EMAIL

NAME

ADDRESS

TEL/FAX

MOBILE

EMAIL

NAME

ADDRESS

TEL/FAX

MOBILE

EMAIL

NAME

ADDRESS

TEL/FAX

MOBILE

EMAIL

NAME

ADDRESS

TEL/FAX

MOBILE

EMAIL

P

NAME

ADDRESS

TEL/FAX

MOBILE

EMAIL

NAME

ADDRESS

TEL/FAX

MOBILE

EMAIL

NAME

ADDRESS

TEL/FAX

MOBILE

EMAIL

NAME

ADDRESS

TEL/FAX

MOBILE

EMAIL

NAME

ADDRESS

TEL/FAX

MOBILE

EMAIL

NAME

ADDRESS

TEL/FAX

MOBILE

EMAIL

NAME

ADDRESS

TEL/FAX

MOBILE

EMAIL

NAME

ADDRESS

TEL/FAX

MOBILE

EMAIL

NAME

ADDRESS

TEL/FAX

MOBILE

EMAIL

NAME

ADDRESS

TEL/FAX

MOBILE

EMAIL

NAME

ADDRESS

TEL/FAX

MOBILE

EMAIL

NAME

ADDRESS

TEL/FAX

MOBILE

EMAIL

NAME

ADDRESS

TEL/FAX

MOBILE

EMAIL

NAME

ADDRESS

TEL/FAX

MOBILE

EMAIL

NAME

ADDRESS

TEL/FAX

MOBILE

EMAIL

NAME

ADDRESS

TEL/FAX

MOBILE

EMAIL

NAME

ADDRESS

TEL/FAX

MOBILE

EMAIL

NAME

ADDRESS

TEL/FAX

MOBILE

EMAIL

NAME

ADDRESS

TEL/FAX

MOBILE

EMAIL

Stork's-Bill, Holy Island, 1901

NAME

ADDRESS

TEL/FAX

MOBILE

EMAIL

NAME

ADDRESS

TEL/FAX

MOBILE

EMAIL

NAME

ADDRESS

TEL/FAX

MOBILE

EMAIL

NAME

ADDRESS

TEL/FAX

MOBILE

EMAIL

NAME

ADDRESS

TEL/FAX

MOBILE

EMAIL

NAME

ADDRESS

TEL/FAX

MOBILE

EMAIL

R

NAME

ADDRESS

TEL/FAX

MOBILE

EMAIL

NAME

ADDRESS

TEL/FAX

MOBILE

EMAIL

NAME

ADDRESS

TEL/FAX

MOBILE

EMAIL

NAME

ADDRESS

TEL/FAX

MOBILE

EMAIL

NAME

ADDRESS

TEL/FAX

MOBILE

EMAIL

NAME

ADDRESS

TEL/FAX

MOBILE

EMAIL

NAME

ADDRESS

TEL/FAX

MOBILE

EMAIL

NAME

ADDRESS

TEL/FAX

MOBILE

EMAIL

NAME

ADDRESS

TEL/FAX

MOBILE

EMAIL

NAME

ADDRESS

TEL/FAX

MOBILE

EMAIL

NAME

ADDRESS

TEL/FAX

MOBILE

EMAIL

NAME

ADDRESS

TEL/FAX

MOBILE

EMAIL

NAME

ADDRESS

TEL/FAX

MOBILE

EMAIL

NAME

ADDRESS

TEL/FAX

MOBILE

EMAIL

NAME

ADDRESS

TEL/FAX

MOBILE

EMAIL

NAME

ADDRESS

TEL/FAX

MOBILE

EMAIL

NAME

ADDRESS

TEL/FAX

MOBILE

EMAIL

NAME

ADDRESS

TEL/FAX

MOBILE

EMAIL

R

Willow Herb, Buxted, 1919

NAME

ADDRESS

TEL/FAX

MOBILE

EMAIL

NAME

ADDRESS

TEL/FAX

MOBILE

EMAIL

NAME

ADDRESS

TEL/FAX

MOBILE

EMAIL

NAME

ADDRESS

TEL/FAX

MOBILE

EMAIL

NAME

ADDRESS

TEL/FAX

MOBILE

EMAIL

NAME

ADDRESS

TEL/FAX

MOBILE

EMAIL

S

NAME

ADDRESS

TEL/FAX

MOBILE

EMAIL

NAME

ADDRESS

TEL/FAX

MOBILE

EMAIL

S

NAME

ADDRESS

TEL/FAX

MOBILE

EMAIL

NAME

ADDRESS

TEL/FAX

MOBILE

EMAIL

NAME

ADDRESS

TEL/FAX

MOBILE

EMAIL

NAME

ADDRESS

TEL/FAX

MOBILE

EMAIL

NAME

ADDRESS

TEL/FAX

MOBILE

EMAIL

NAME

ADDRESS

TEL/FAX

MOBILE

EMAIL

NAME

ADDRESS

TEL/FAX

MOBILE

EMAIL

NAME

ADDRESS

TEL/FAX

MOBILE

EMAIL

NAME

ADDRESS

TEL/FAX

MOBILE

EMAIL

NAME

ADDRESS

TEL/FAX

MOBILE

EMAIL

NAME

ADDRESS

TEL/FAX

MOBILE

EMAIL

NAME

ADDRESS

TEL/FAX

MOBILE

EMAIL

NAME

ADDRESS

TEL/FAX

MOBILE

EMAIL

NAME

ADDRESS

TEL/FAX

MOBILE

EMAIL

NAME

ADDRESS

TEL/FAX

MOBILE

EMAIL

NAME

ADDRESS

TEL/FAX

MOBILE

EMAIL

S

Sea Pink, Holy Island, July 1901

NAME

ADDRESS

TEL/FAX

MOBILE

EMAIL

NAME

ADDRESS

TEL/FAX

MOBILE

EMAIL

NAME

ADDRESS

TEL/FAX

MOBILE

EMAIL

NAME

ADDRESS

TEL/FAX

MOBILE

EMAIL

NAME

ADDRESS

TEL/FAX

MOBILE

EMAIL

NAME

ADDRESS

TEL/FAX

MOBILE

EMAIL

NAME

ADDRESS

TEL/FAX

MOBILE

EMAIL

NAME

ADDRESS

TEL/FAX

MOBILE

EMAIL

T

NAME

ADDRESS

TEL/FAX

MOBILE

EMAIL

NAME

ADDRESS

TEL/FAX

MOBILE

EMAIL

NAME

ADDRESS

TEL/FAX

MOBILE

EMAIL

NAME

ADDRESS

TEL/FAX

MOBILE

EMAIL

NAME

ADDRESS

TEL/FAX

MOBILE

EMAIL

NAME

ADDRESS

TEL/FAX

MOBILE

EMAIL

NAME

ADDRESS

TEL/FAX

MOBILE

EMAIL

NAME

ADDRESS

TEL/FAX

MOBILE

EMAIL

NAME

ADDRESS

TEL/FAX

MOBILE

EMAIL

NAME

ADDRESS

TEL/FAX

MOBILE

EMAIL

NAME

ADDRESS

TEL/FAX

MOBILE

EMAIL

NAME

ADDRESS

TEL/FAX

MOBILE

EMAIL

NAME

ADDRESS

TEL/FAX

MOBILE

EMAIL

NAME

ADDRESS

TEL/FAX

MOBILE

EMAIL

NAME

ADDRESS

TEL/FAX

MOBILE

EMAIL

NAME

ADDRESS

TEL/FAX

MOBILE

EMAIL

U
V

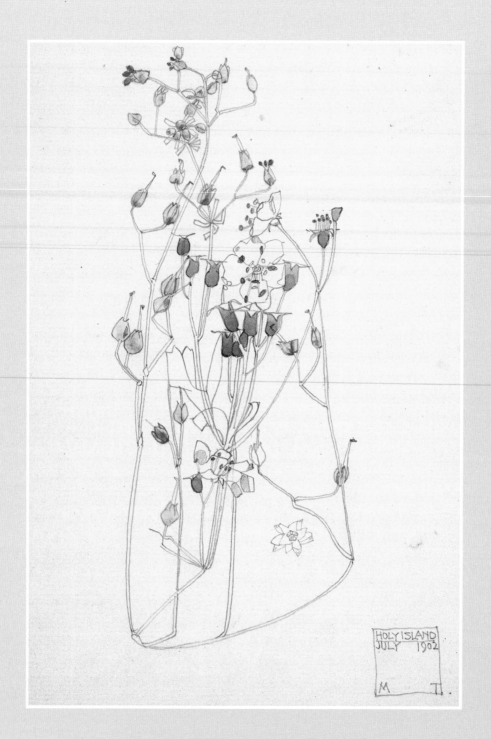

Crane's-Bill, Holy Island, 1902

NAME

ADDRESS

TEL/FAX

MOBILE

EMAIL

NAME

ADDRESS

TEL/FAX

MOBILE

EMAIL

NAME

ADDRESS

TEL/FAX

MOBILE

EMAIL

NAME

ADDRESS

TEL/FAX

MOBILE

EMAIL

NAME

ADDRESS

TEL/FAX

MOBILE

EMAIL

NAME

ADDRESS

TEL/FAX

MOBILE

EMAIL

NAME

ADDRESS

TEL/FAX

MOBILE

EMAIL

NAME

ADDRESS

TEL/FAX

MOBILE

EMAIL

NAME

ADDRESS

TEL/FAX

MOBILE

EMAIL

NAME

ADDRESS

TEL/FAX

MOBILE

EMAIL

NAME

ADDRESS

TEL/FAX

MOBILE

EMAIL

NAME

ADDRESS

TEL/FAX

MOBILE

EMAIL

NAME

ADDRESS

TEL/FAX

MOBILE

EMAIL

NAME

ADDRESS

TEL/FAX

MOBILE

EMAIL

NAME

ADDRESS

TEL/FAX

MOBILE

EMAIL

NAME

ADDRESS

TEL/FAX

MOBILE

EMAIL

NAME

ADDRESS

TEL/FAX

MOBILE

EMAIL

NAME	NAME
ADDRESS	ADDRESS
TEL/FAX	TEL/FAX
MOBILE	MOBILE
EMAIL	EMAIL
NAME	NAME
ADDRESS	ADDRESS
TEL/FAX	TEL/FAX
MOBILE	MOBILE
EMAIL	EMAIL
NAME	NAME
ADDRESS	ADDRESS
TEL/FAX	TEL/FAX
MOBILE	MOBILE
EMAIL	EMAIL
NAME	NAME
ADDRESS	ADDRESS
TEL/FAX	TEL/FAX
MOBILE	MOBILE
EMAIL	EMAIL
NAME	NAME
ADDRESS	ADDRESS
TEL/FAX	TEL/FAX
MOBILE	MOBILE
EMAIL	EMAIL

Spurge, Withyham, 1909

NAME

ADDRESS

TEL/FAX

MOBILE

EMAIL

NAME

ADDRESS

TEL/FAX

MOBILE

EMAIL

NAME

ADDRESS

TEL/FAX

MOBILE

EMAIL

NAME

ADDRESS

TEL/FAX

MOBILE

EMAIL

NAME

ADDRESS

TEL/FAX

MOBILE

EMAIL

X
Y
Z

NAME

ADDRESS

TEL/FAX

MOBILE

EMAIL

NAME

ADDRESS

TEL/FAX

MOBILE

EMAIL

NAME

ADDRESS

TEL/FAX

MOBILE

EMAIL

NAME

ADDRESS

TEL/FAX

MOBILE

EMAIL

NOTES

Flower Drawings Photographs © Hunterian Art Gallery,
University of Glasgow, Mackintosh Collection

Designed and Published in Scotland by
Colin Baxter Photography
Grantown-on-Spey PH26 3NA
Printed in Hong Kong
ISBN 1-84107-128-5

Front Cover picture: Mimosa, Amélie-Les-Bains, January 1924

Back Cover picture: Fritillaria, Walberswick, 1915